Houghton Mifflin

WOW!
Wonder of Words

LITERACY ACTIVITY BOOK

Senior Authors	**Authors**	**Consultants**
J. David Cooper	Kathryn H. Au	Dolores Malcolm
John J. Pikulski	Margarita Calderón	Tina Saldivar
	Jacqueline C. Comas	Shane Templeton
	Marjorie Y. Lipson	
	J. Sabrina Mims	
	Susan E. Page	
	Sheila W. Valencia	
	MaryEllen Vogt	

INVITATIONS TO LITERACY

Houghton Mifflin Company • Boston

Atlanta • Dallas • Geneva, Illinois • Palo Alto • Princeton

1997 Impression
Copyright © 1996 by Houghton Mifflin Company. All rights reserved.

Printed in the U.S.A

ISBN: 0-395-75032-6

56789-WC-99 98 97

CONTENTS

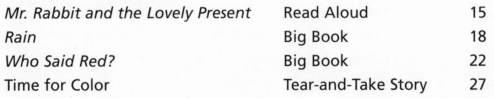

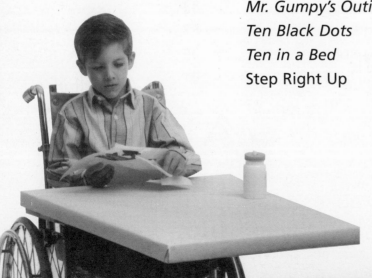

CONTENTS

CONTENTS

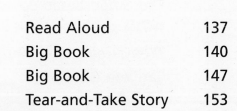

CONTENTS

All About Me

On Monday When It Rained
PERSONAL RESPONSE
Have children imagine they are at a playground like the one in the story. Have them draw pictures of themselves that show how they feel about being there.

Dear Family,
Play a pantomime game with your child. Take turns acting out an event of the day using facial expressions to show feelings about what happened. Guess what the other person is acting out.

1

On Monday When It Rained
COMPREHENSION Noting Details

Reread page 11 of the story to children. Then ask them to draw a picture of the kind of animal that the boy in the story drew.

All About Me

2

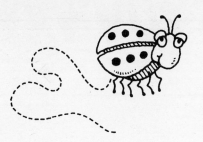  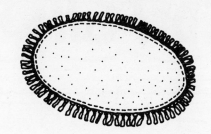

  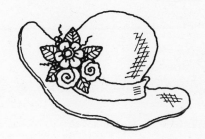

All About Me

On Monday When It Rained
PHONEMIC AWARENESS Rhyme

Have children name the pictures in the first row. (*bug, ball, rug*) Then ask, **Which picture names have the same last sounds?** Have children put a circle around *bug* and a circle around *rug* to show that they have the same last sounds. Then continue with Row 2 for *car, cat, hat,* and Row 3 for *dog, frog, door.*

ABCDEFGHIJKLMNOPQRSTUVWXYZ

ABCDEFGHIJKLMNOPQRSTUVWXYZ

All About Me

ABC and You
PERSONAL RESPONSE

Tell children they can make a page about themselves that is like the pages about the children in *ABC and You*. Say, **Write the first letter of your name in the box. Beside the letter, draw a picture of you that shows something you do a lot. Then write your name on the line below your picture.**

4

C   Crying _____

A   Angry _____

D   Dancing _____

S   Sleepy _____

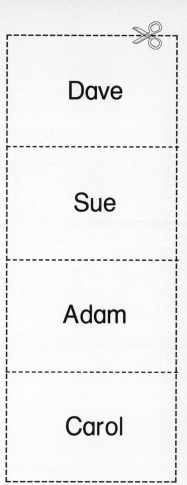

Dave

Sue

Adam

Carol

All About Me

ABC and You
LANGUAGE PATTERNS

Have children name the letter and trace it. Have them tell about each picture. Then read aloud the word beside the picture. Have children paste the name that starts with the same letter on the line beside the word.

5

6

All About Me

ABC and You
COMPREHENSION Sequence

Say, **Avery, Ben, Cathy, and Don want to show the first four letters of the alphabet. Avery is holding the letter A, because it comes first in the alphabet and because it's the first letter of his name.** Have children trace the letter A and print the letters the other children should be holding.

A B C D E F G H I J K L M N O P Q R S T U V W X Y Z

All About Me

ABC and You
CONCEPT DEVELOPMENT Naming Capital Letters

Say, Take your pencil on an alphabet walk. Start with *A*, and stop to name each letter you pass. You can ask about letters whose names you don't know.

Dear Family,

Look together through the headlines in an old newspaper. Find and cut out an example of each letter of the alphabet. Then work together to arrange them in ABC order.

All About Me

Faces
PERSONAL RESPONSE
Ask children to think about the face of someone who is very special to them and have them draw the face inside the frame. Then, below their picture, have them write or dictate something they would like to tell about the person.

faces seeing,

faces hearing,

faces smelling.

All About Me

Faces
LANGUAGE PATTERNS
Have children describe what the girl in the first picture is doing. (looking at a butterfly)
Read aloud the phrase from the selection and have children draw what the girl is using
to see with. Repeat for the remaining phrases, having children draw pictures of what
the boy is using to hear with and what the woman is using to smell with.

Faces

COMPREHENSION Categorize and Classify

Say, **The children going out into the sunshine both feel the same way. The children who can't go out because it's raining all feel the same way.** Have children draw in the faces on each group to show how everyone feels.

All About Me

11

Faces

CONCEPT DEVELOPMENT Naming Facial Features and Body Parts

Tell children to draw a picture of themselves doing something they like to do outside on a warm, sunny day. Ask them to circle on their picture their feet, their knees, their hands, or their heads. Then have them write or dictate labels for the body parts they circled.

All About Me

12

Dear Family,
Invite your child to tell you the story *Just Right for Me.* Then make a picture story together about something your child thinks is just right for him or her.

4

FOLD HERE

Just Right for Me

1

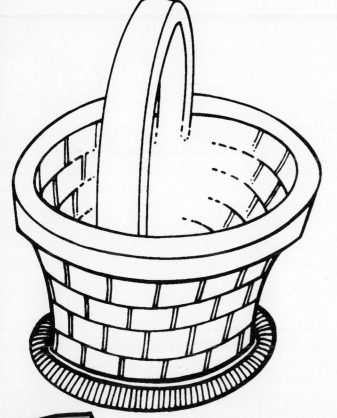

Color Is Everywhere

Mr. Rabbit and the Lovely Present
PERSONAL RESPONSE

Tell the children that this is a basket like the little girl's basket in the story. Then say, **Draw what you might like to receive in a basket.**

Dear Family,
Invite your child to tell you the story *Mr. Rabbit and the Lovely Present*. Then have him or her tell the story again, this time changing what goes into the birthday basket.

Mr. Rabbit and the Lovely Present
COMPREHENSION Inferences: Making Predictions

Have the children color one paint spot red, one green, one yellow, and one blue.
Remind them that the girl's mother liked fruits that were these colors. Then say,
**Beside each color spot, draw something else the girl's mother might like that is the
same color.**

**Color Is
Everywhere**

16

Color Is Everywhere

Mr. Rabbit and the Lovely Present
PHONEMIC AWARENESS Rhyming Words

Help children name the pictures in each row (*tree, bee, bird; cup, boat, coat; fork, fan, can*). Have them color the two in each row that rhyme.

Rain
PERSONAL RESPONSE

Have children draw a picture of themselves doing something they like
to do in the rain.

**Color Is
Everywhere**

Rain _____

Color Is Everywhere

Rain
LANGUAGE PATTERNS

Children think of an object on which the rain can fall and what happens to it when it gets wet. They draw and color their picture and then, using the language pattern from the story, write or dictate a phrase to describe their picture.

Rain

COMPREHENSION Story Structure: Beginning, Middle, End

In the first space, children show how the sky looked at the beginning of the story. In the second space, they show how the sky looked in the middle of the story. In the third space, they show how the sky looked at the end of the story.

Color Is
Everywhere

20

yellow sun

green tree

black road

red car

Rain

CONCEPT DEVELOPMENT Color Words

Read aloud the color word labels for each item. Then have children color each item according to its label. Invite them to draw one more yellow, green, black or red thing on the page.

Color Is Everywhere

Dear Family,
On your next walk together, take along paper and colored markers or crayons. Take turns drawing and coloring pictures of things you see. When you get home, write the color words on each picture as your child tells you its color.

21

Who Said Red?
PERSONAL RESPONSE

Children draw and color a picture of something that is their favorite color. They may wish to write or dictate a phrase or sentence that tells about their picture.

red　　brown

yellow　white

green　black

blue　　pink

_____

- -

Who said _____?

_____

- -

I said _____!

Color Is Everywhere

Who Said Red?
LANGUAGE PATTERNS

Read aloud the color words with children. Then have them write the word that names a color from the story to complete the sentences. Invite them to draw a picture of something that is usually that color.

yellow red blue

Who Said Red?
COMPREHENSION Inferences: Drawing Conclusions

Read aloud the color words on each crayon and have children color the crayon that color. Then ask them to color: the boy's hair red, his socks red, his rain pants red, and his kite red; his shirt blue; and his shorts yellow. Invite children to look at the pictures and decide which color is probably the boy's favorite color. Have them circle the crayon that matches his favorite color and write the color name on the lines.

Color Is Everywhere

24

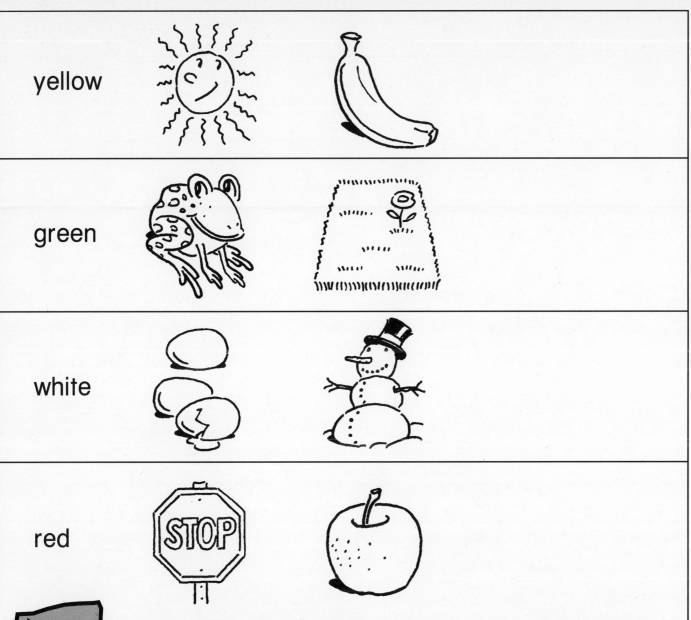

yellow		
green		
white		
red		

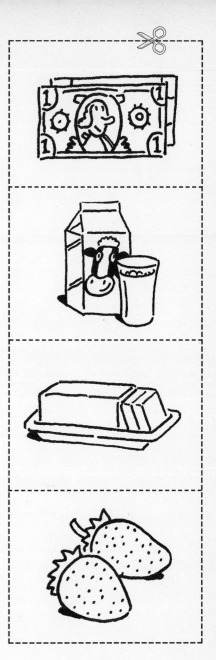

Color Is Everywhere

Who Said Red?
CONCEPT DEVELOPMENT Color Words

Children color the pictures in the rows with the color words as you read each word aloud (*yellow*: sun, banana; *green*: frog, grass; *white*: eggs, snowman; *red*: stop sign, apple). They name and color the remaining pictures the color each should be and paste these pictures beside the other pictures of the same color. Children do not need to color items that should be white.

25

Dear Family,
Work with your child to make a "Rainbow Closet" by hanging his or her clothes in color groups, side by side on the closet rod.

4

FOLD HERE

Time for Color

1

2

3

FOLD HERE

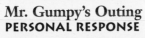

Just for Fun

Mr. Gumpy's Outing
PERSONAL RESPONSE
Children talk about the faces and tell which one best shows how they feel about the story. They add hair and other details to the face they choose to make a self-portrait. Then they draw a picture to show something in the story that made them feel that way.

Dear Family,
Invite your child to retell the story *Mr. Gumpy's Outing* to you. Then make up a different version of the story in which Mr. Gumpy tells each animal, "No," instead of "Yes," when they ask to go along.

Mr. Gumpy's Outing
COMPREHENSION Noting Details

Children decide which of the pictures at the top of the page show characters that got into the boat in the story but who are not in the boat in this picture (the man, the girl and boy, the cat). Then they draw the missing characters in the boat with the other characters from the story.

Just for Fun

30

Just for Fun

Mr. Gumpy's Outing
PHONEMIC AWARENESS Words that Rhyme

Children look at the picture and listen for the rhyming words as you say this silly sentence that describes it: **A goat in a boat is wearing a coat.** They think up and illustrate another silly sentence using words that rhyme with *cat*. Children may wish to write or dictate their silly sentence.

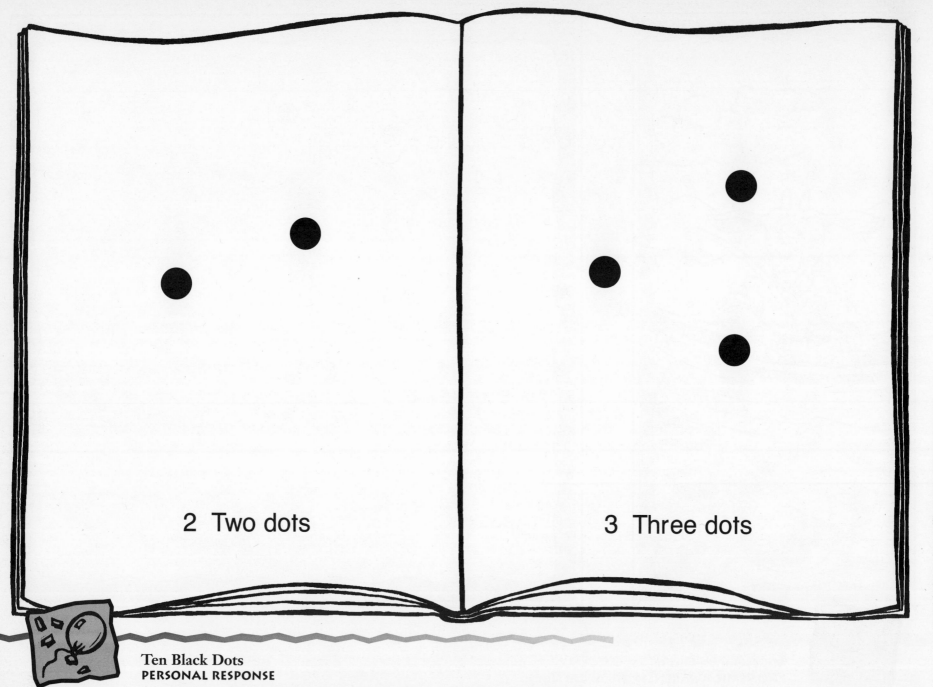

2 Two dots

3 Three dots

Ten Black Dots
PERSONAL RESPONSE
Ask children to draw around each set of black dots to make a picture they would
want to put in a number book like *Ten Black Dots.*

Just for Fun

1   One dot can make a  .

2   Two dots can make  .

 dots can make

4 Four dots can make

Just for Fun

Ten Black Dots
LANGUAGE PATTERNS
Ask children to identify the rebus pictures at the end of the first two sentences (bee, keys). Then read these sentences aloud. Read the number words on the next two lines, having children trace the numeral and the word to repeat the language pattern from the selection. Read the incomplete sentences with children and invite them to draw a picture at the end of each one to complete it.

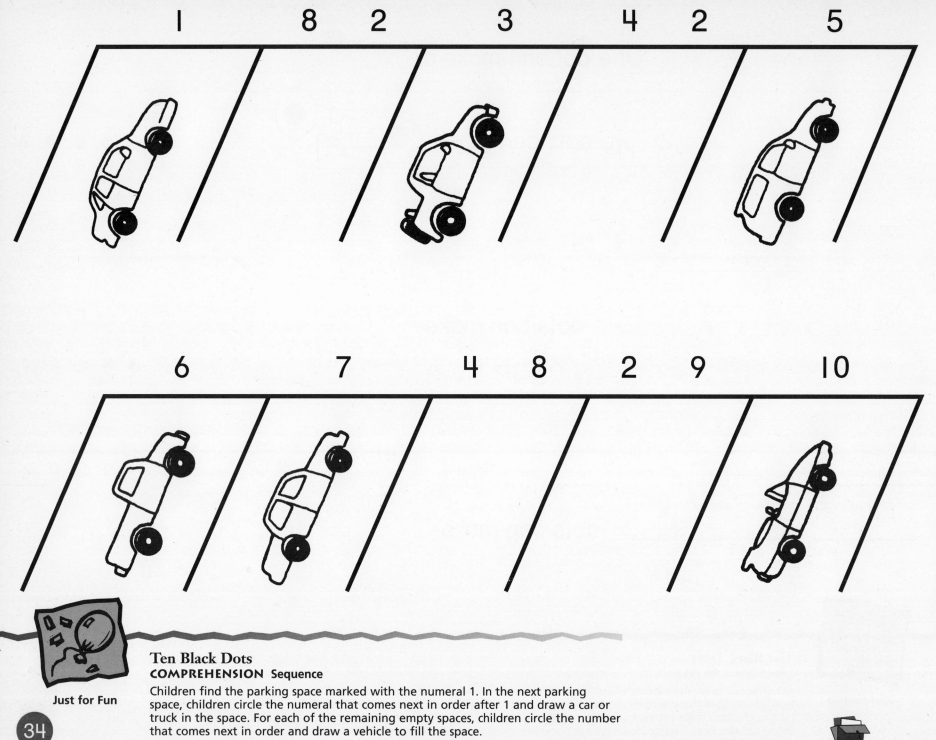

Ten Black Dots
COMPREHENSION Sequence

Children find the parking space marked with the numeral 1. In the next parking space, children circle the numeral that comes next in order after 1 and draw a car or truck in the space. For each of the remaining empty spaces, children circle the number that comes next in order and draw a vehicle to fill the space.

Just for Fun

34

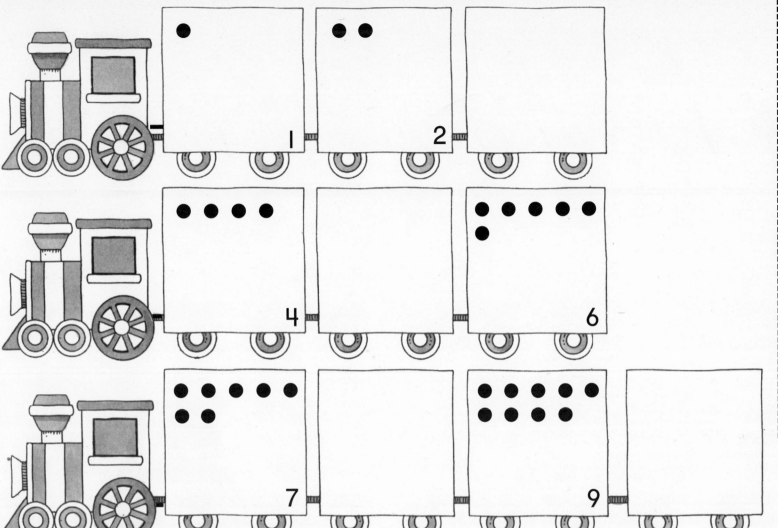

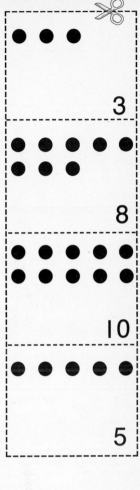

Just for Fun

Ten Black Dots

CONCEPT DEVELOPMENT Numeral Identification

Tell children that the engines are pulling loads of dots — each box with one more dot than the box before it. Ask children to decide how many dots should go in the empty boxes. Have them cut and paste a dot box that has the right number of dots in each empty box.

Dear Family,

On your next trip to the market together, take along a pencil and a paper with numbers 1 through 10 written on it. Take turns looking for and checking off each number as you spot it on signs in the store.

35

Ten in a Bed
PERSONAL RESPONSE

Have children draw a picture of their favorite part of the story. You may wish to have them write or dictate a sentence telling about their picture.

Just for Fun

37

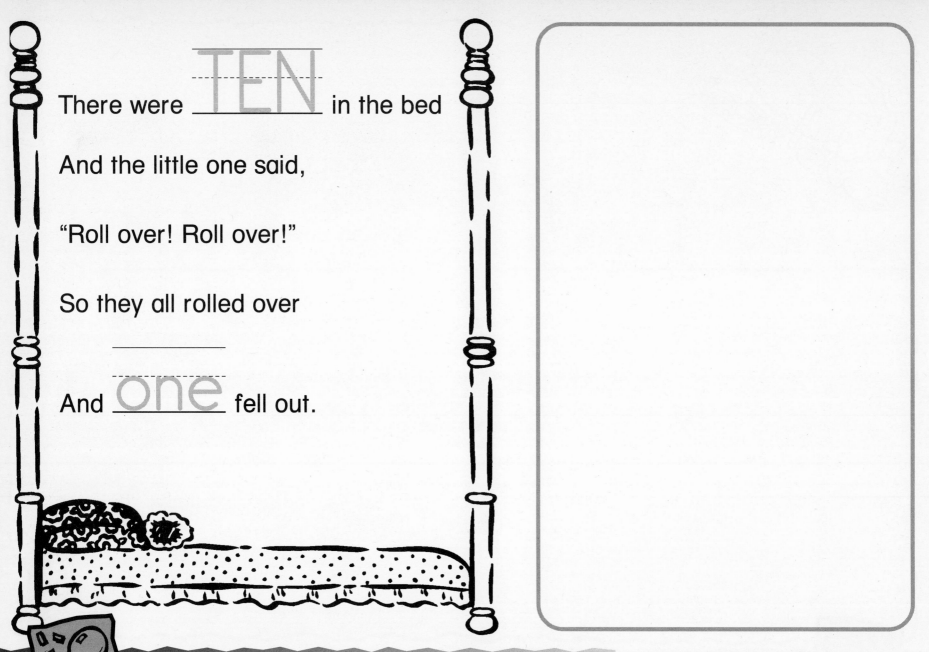

There were ___TEN___ in the bed

And the little one said,

"Roll over! Roll over!"

So they all rolled over

_____

And ___one___ fell out.

Ten in a Bed
LANGUAGE PATTERNS
Have children trace the number words in the blanks to complete the language pattern. Then ask them to illustrate one part of the story, using characters different from those in the story, for example monkeys, elephants, or ducks.

Just for Fun

38

Just for Fun

Ten in a Bed
COMPREHENSION Cause and Effect
Have children describe what is happening in the picture. Then have them draw a
picture to show what they think happened to make the block building fall.

39

4

3

2

1

Just for Fun

Ten in a Bed
CONCEPT DEVELOPMENT Number/Object Equivalents

Children find the top row and listen as you say, **There were five in a bed and the little one said, "Roll over! Roll over!"** Children respond by cutting on the broken line and folding back on the solid lines to demonstrate what happened when one fell out. Children continue to cut and fold back the end of each row as each of the remaining lines is read or sung.

41

42

Dear Family,
Take a walk in your neighborhood or in a town. Together count the steps on some of the houses or buildings to find out which have the most steps. When you get home, count the steps at the front of your own home.

4

Step Right Up

FOLD HERE

1

2

3

A Birthday Basket for _____

Family Time

A Birthday Basket for Tía
PERSONAL RESPONSE

Children name a family member they'd like to give a birthday basket to and write the person's name to complete the phrase *A Birthday Basket for* ____. They draw, inside the basket outline, things they'd give this person.

Dear Family,
Invite your child to tell you about the story *A Birthday Basket for Tía*. Then talk about the birthday basket your child created on this page for a family member.

45

Cecilia	Cecilia and Tía	Tía

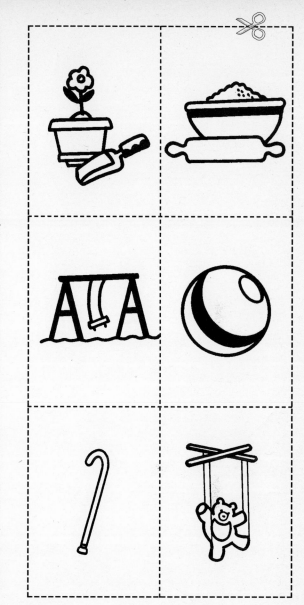

Family Time

A Birthday Basket for Tía
COMPREHENSION Compare
and Contrast

Read aloud the names of the story characters at the top of each column and have
children identify the pictures they will cut out (gardening things, cooking things,
swing, ball, cane, puppet). Ask them to paste the pictures that tell something about
both Cecilia and Tía in the center column and to paste the pictures that show
something about Cecilia only in the first column and about Tía only in the last column.

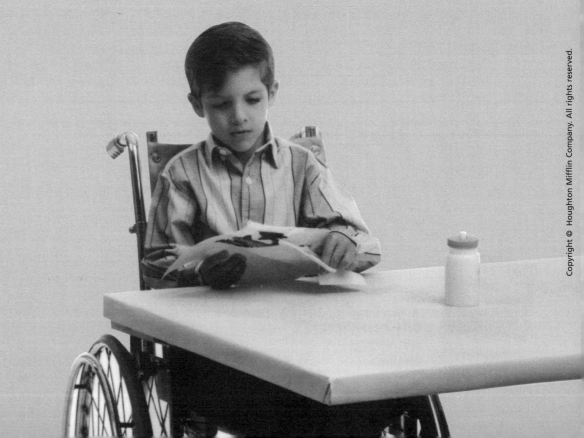

A Birthday Basket for Tía
PHONEMIC AWARENESS Beginning Sounds

Family Time

Tell children that Cecilia is planning a big birthday basket for someone else and that she wants to put in it pairs of things whose names begin with the same sounds. Help children name the pictures in each row and circle the two whose names have the same beginning sound to show what Cecilia will put in this basket (*cake, rake, candy; cat, ball, bat; pan, puppet, fan; necklace, net, jet*).

 49

Animal Mothers
PERSONAL RESPONSE
Children name the animal mothers from the selection that are shown in the borders.
They choose the animal they like best and draw a picture of that animal. Children
may wish to write or dictate something about their picture.

Family Time

50

lion

chimp

zebra

koala

_____

- -

Mother _____

Family Time

Animal Mothers
LANGUAGE PATTERNS
Children identify the animal mothers pictured. They choose one and draw a picture showing that mother with her baby. Then, using the language pattern from the selection, children complete the sentence by writing or dictating the name of the animal and words that tell how she keeps her baby close.

51

Animal Mothers

COMPREHENSION Text Organization: Noting Details

Children identify the animals in the pictures. Then children draw a picture that shows something they learned from the selection about one of the animals. Children may wish to write or dictate more details about what they have chosen to draw.

Family Time

m

Animal Mothers
PHONICS/DECODING *m*
Children think of the sound at the begining of the Magic Picture *monster* as they name and trace the letter *m*. They color the pictures that begin with the sound for *m* (*motorcycle, moon, mailbox, mitten, mop, magnet*), print the letter beside each, and draw a line from the mouse to her nest by following the pictures.

Family Time

Dear Family,
We have been learning about the letter *m* and the sound it stands for. Ask your child to tell you about this page. Then ask your child to help you find things in your home that begin with the sound for *m* and write a list of what you find.

53

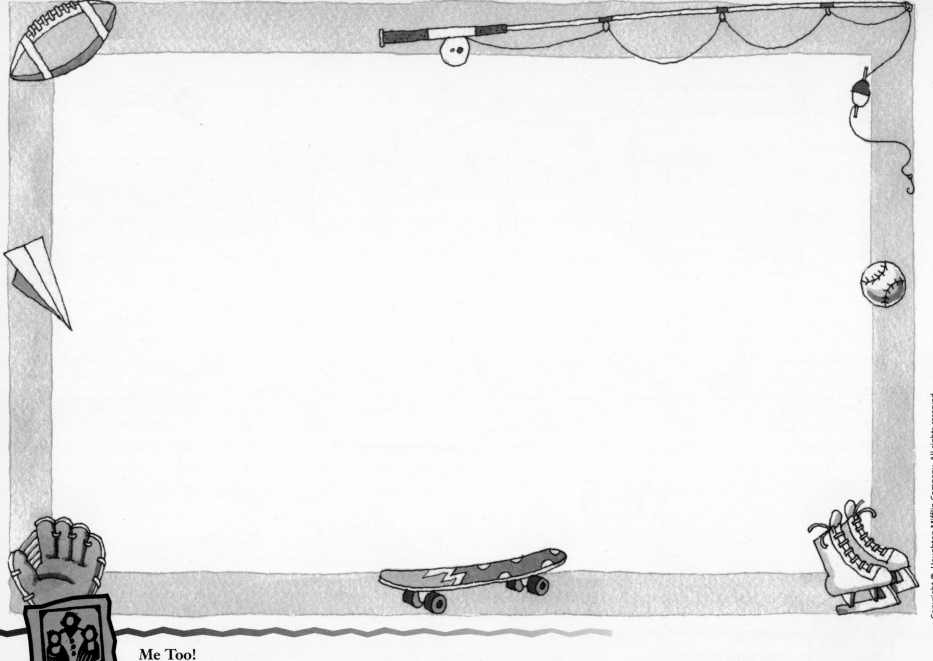

Me Too!
PERSONAL RESPONSE
Children draw a picture to show an activity from the story that they would like to do. They may wish to write or dictate a sentence about their picture. If children choose to draw and write about a different activity, permit them to do so.

Family Time

54

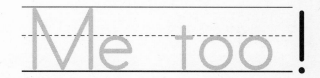

Family Time

Me Too!
LANGUAGE PATTERNS

Explain that the pictures show activities in the story that the little sister also wanted to do. Have children identify the activities and trace the words *Me too* next to each of the activities.

Children may wish to draw a picture of their own here.

Family Time

Me Too!
COMPREHENSION Fantasy and Realism
Children paste the pictures that show make-believe animals doing things below the
fantasy animals and the pictures that show animals doing things that real animals do
below the real-looking animals.

S S S

Me too!

Family Time

Me Too!
PHONICS/DECODING *s*

Children think of the sound at the beginning of the Magic Picture *seal* as they name, trace, and print the letter *s* at the top of the page. Then they search the beach scene for pictures whose names begin with the sound for *s* and color those that they find (*seal, socks, sandals, sun, sandcastle, sandwiches*).

59

I ____said____, "____My____ 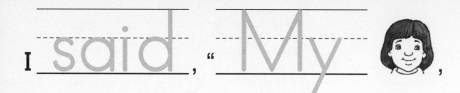,

"____my____ ,

"____my____ ."

"____My____ ," I ____said____.

Family Time

Me Too!
VOCABULARY High-Frequency Words: *said, my*

Children identify who the rebus pictures at the end of each sentence might represent in their own families—mother, aunt, grandfather, uncle, brother, sister, or cousin. They trace the words on the lines and read the sentences. They may wish to write or dictate an additional sentence at the bottom of the page.

60

My Family

"My ," said .

Dear Family,
Look through old family photos with your child, naming those he or she may not recognize. Explain how these people are related to your child.

"My ," said .

FOLD HERE

◇2◇ "My ," said .

"My ," said . ◇3◇

In the Barnyard

The Rain Puddle
PERSONAL RESPONSE

Children draw pictures of favorite animals from *The Rain Puddle*. They may wish to write or dictate words to label their pictures.

Dear Family,

Look through old magazines to find pictures of farm animals your child can name. Together you might want to cut out the pictures and paste them on pages to make your own book about farm animals.

63

" _____ "

- -

Owl said, _____ .

In the Barnyard

The Rain Puddle
COMPREHENSION Inferences: Drawing Conclusions
Children draw a picture to show what the wise old owl might have seen, had **he** looked into the rain puddle. Invite them to write or dictate what the wise old owl might have said about what he saw there.

64

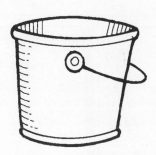

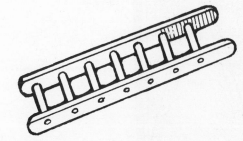

In the Barnyard

The Rain Puddle
PHONEMIC AWARENESS Beginning Sounds

Help children name the three pictures in each row *(barn, boy, yarn; wig, pig, pail; jam, lamb, ladder)*. Have them color in each row the two pictures whose names begin with the same sound.

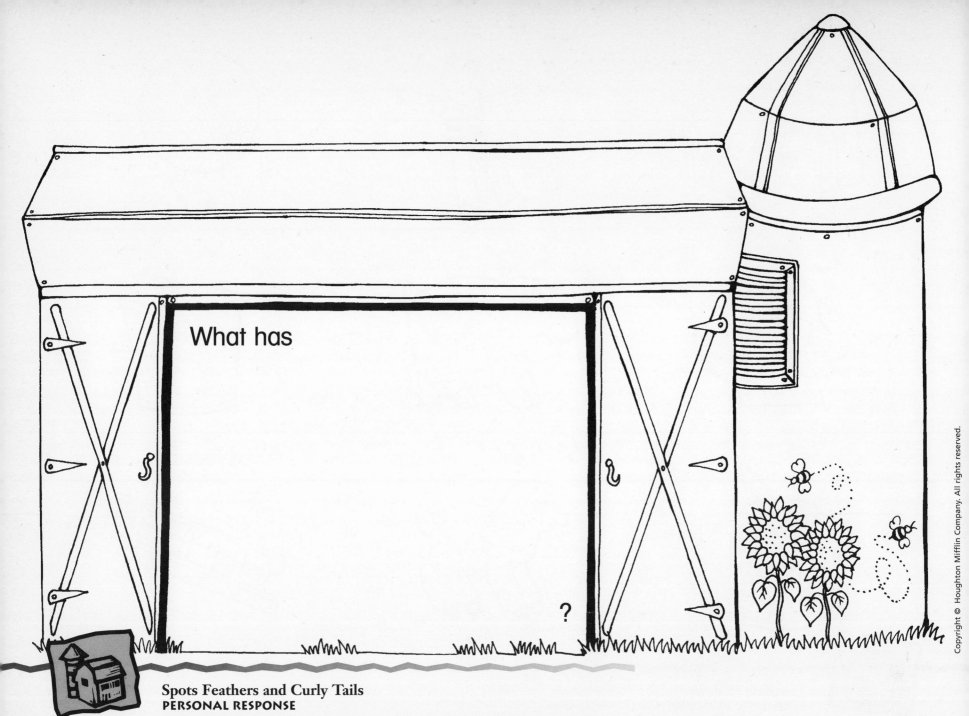

What has

?

Spots Feathers and Curly Tails
PERSONAL RESPONSE
Children think of an animal from the story or some other animal they know about and draw only one part of it inside the open barn door. Then they exchange papers with others and answer each other's questions.

In the Barnyard

66

What has spots?
A cow has spots.

What

has

_____

_____?

A

_____

_____

has

_____

_____.

In the Barnyard

Spots Feathers and Curly Tails
LANGUAGE PATTERNS

Read aloud the language pattern from the story. Ask children to write or dictate words to complete the sentences on the first and third panels. On the second panel, have them illustrate the animal part they name and on the last panel, the whole animal. Demonstrate how to make an accordion book by cutting out the whole piece and folding along the solid lines.

In the Barnyard

Spots Feathers and Curly Tails
COMPREHENSION Inferences: Making Predictions

Children name each part of an animal shown in the first column (beard or face, tail, head) and think about what the whole animal would be. Then they identify the animals in the cut-out boxes (turkey, sheep, goat) and paste each animal picture beside the animal part.

h h _____ h

_____ h

In the Barnyard

Spots Feathers and Curly Tails
PHONICS/DECODING *h*
Children think of the sound at the beginning of the Magic Picture *horse* as they name and trace the letter *h*. They name the pictures and write the letter *h* by those whose names begin with the sound for *h* (*house, hat, helicopter, hammer, hose, hook*). Then they color in each *h* puzzle piece to form a large *h*.

Dear Family,
We have been learning about the letter *h* and the sound it stands for. Invite your child to tell you about this page. As you read picture books together, keep track of words you find that start with the sound for *h*.

71

the cow

the pig

the horse

the bull

In the Barnyard

Spots Feathers and Curly Tails
VOCABULARY High-Frequency Words: *the*

Read the labels aloud with children, having them trace the word *the* to complete each one. Suggest that children color the pictures of the animals they like best.

72

I Love Animals
PERSONAL RESPONSE

Children draw a picture of something from the story that they have seen in real life.
They may wish to write or dictate a sentence about what they drew.

In the Barnyard

I love _____.

_____

- -

I love _____.

In the Barnyard

I Love Animals
LANGUAGE PATTERNS
Read the language pattern from the story with children and have them think of an animal to complete the sentence. Ask them to draw a picture of themselves with the animal they have chosen. You may wish to have them write or dictate a word to complete the sentence at the bottom of the page.

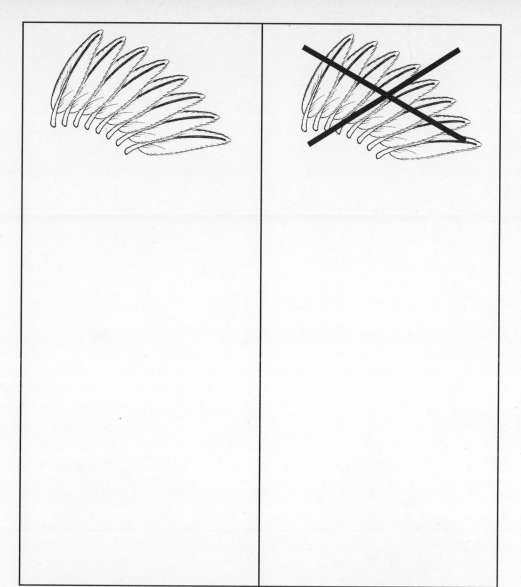

In the Barnyard

I Love Animals
COMPREHENSION Categorize and Classify

Children name the animals (bird, cow, cat, horse, chicken, turkey) and decide which have feathers (bird, chicken, turkey). They paste the pictures of animals with feathers below the feathers symbol in the first column. They paste the pictures of animals who do not have feathers below the symbol that means no feathers.

75

d d

I Love Animals
PHONICS/DECODING *d*

Children think of the sound at the beginning of the Magic Picture *dinosaur* as they name and trace the letter at the top of the page. They name the pictures in the maze and color each one whose name begins with the sound for *d* (*dog, doll, duck, deer, desk*). They write the letter *d* by each picture they color and draw a line from the dog to his house.

In the Barnyard

mat hat sat

Cat said, "My _____."

Cat said, "My _____."

Cat _____.

"My _____," said  .

In the Barnyard

I Love Animals
PHONICS/DECODING Phonogram: *-at*
Children trace the letters to make words with the phonogram *-at*. They use these words to finish the story about Cat and then they read the story.

78

" I ♥ my 🐱 ," said Pat.

" ___ ♥ my [   ] ," said _____ .

In the Barnyard

I Love Animals
VOCABULARY High-frequency Words: *I*

Help children identify the meaning of the rebus pictures (love, cat). Then have them trace the word *I* and help them read the first sentence. For the last sentence have the children draw a picture of something they love and complete the sentence by writing their own name.

79

Children may wish to draw a picture of their own here.

"The mat!" I said.

4

Dear Family,
Go to the public library together and ask the librarian to help you find picture books about farm animals. Look through the books together and compare the animals.

The Hat

"My hat!" said the .

1

"The hat!" said the

FOLD HERE

"The hat!" said the

Ira Sleeps Over
PERSONAL RESPONSE

Children draw a picture to show something they would like to do if they were sleeping over at a friend's house. Children may wish to write or dictate a sentence about their drawing.

Nighttime

Dear Family,
Talk with your child about what he or she might take along to spend the night at a friend's home. Together make a list of the items and narrow it down to those things he or she thinks would be absolutely necessary to take.

83

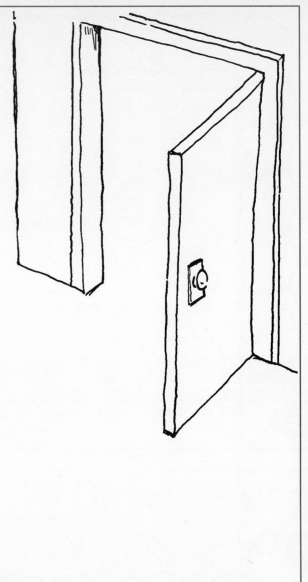

Nighttime

Ira Sleeps Over
COMPREHENSION Story Structure: Character

Ask, **What would Ira do if he was invited to sleep over at another friend's home?**
Have children draw a picture showing Ira either doing something at home or doing
something to get ready to go to his friend's home.

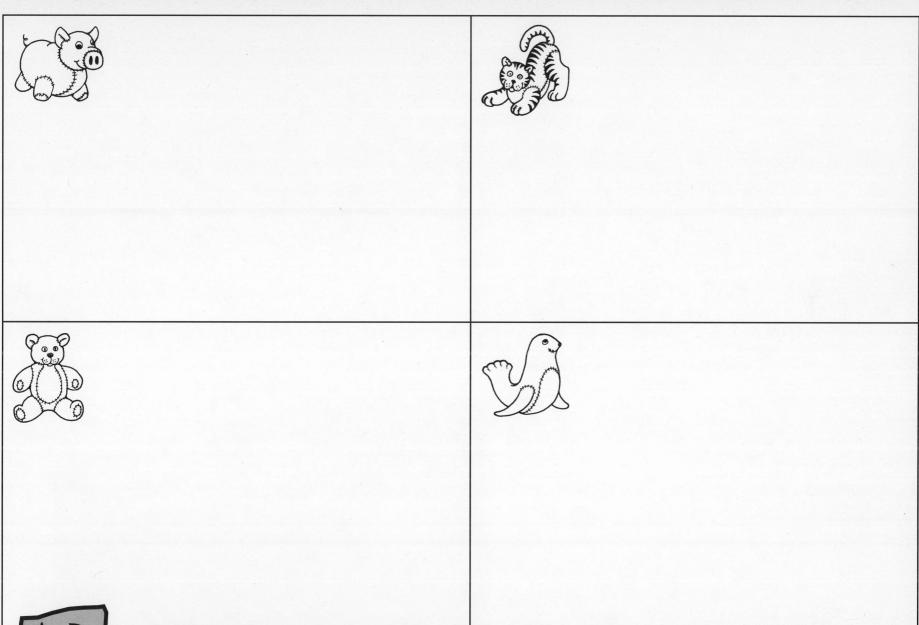

Nighttime

Ira Sleeps Over
PHONEMIC AWARENESS Same Beginning Sounds

For each section, children name the stuffed animal (pig, cat, bear, seal). Next to each stuffed animal, children draw a picture of something else whose name begins with the same sound.

Nighttime

Golden Bear
PERSONAL RESPONSE

Children draw a picture of something the boy and Golden Bear do together that the children would also like to do with a teddy bear or other cuddly toy. They may wish to write or dictate a sentence about their picture.

Golden Bear, Golden Bear,

I have seen him

Golden Bear
LANGUAGE PATTERNS

Read the incomplete language pattern from the story with children and ask them to think of something the bear might be doing in another place not mentioned in the story. Have them illustrate their idea. They may wish to write or dictate words to complete the language pattern to go with their pictures.

Nighttime

Nighttime

Golden Bear
COMPREHENSION Fantasy and Realism

Children tell what is happening in the pictures and tell which shows what a real dog is like and which shows a make-believe dog. They paste the pictures that show what a real dog could do under the picture of the real dog. They paste pictures that show what a make-believe dog might do under the picture of the make-believe dog.

90

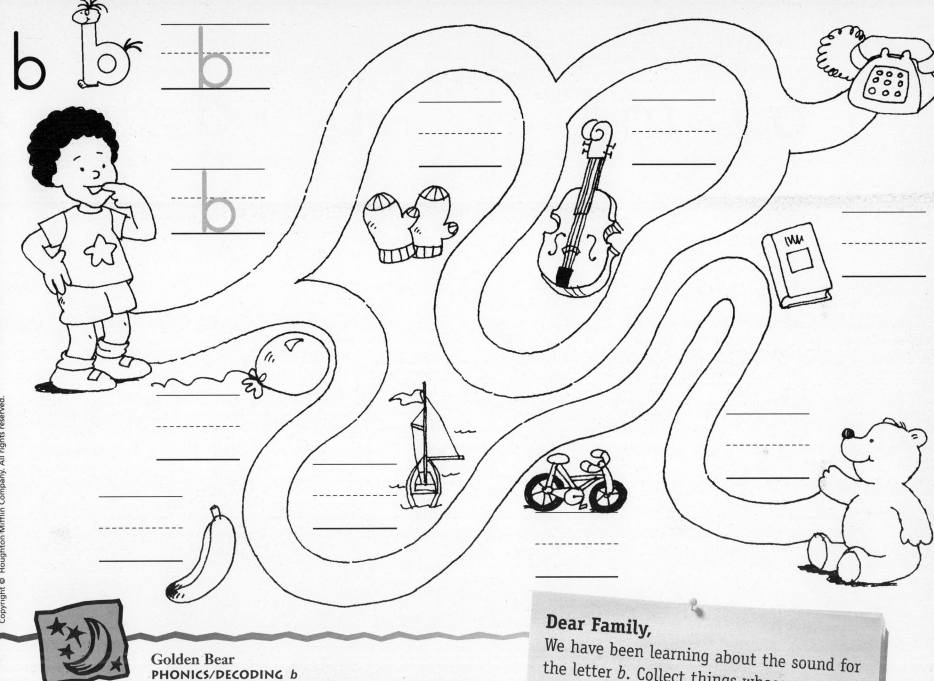

Nighttime

Golden Bear
PHONICS/DECODING *b*

Children think of the sound at the beginning of the Magic Picture *bird* as they name and trace the letter. They color the pictures that begin with the sound for *b* (*boy, balloon, banana, boat, bicycle, book, bear*), write the letter *b* next to those pictures, and draw a line from the boy to his bear.

Dear Family,
We have been learning about the sound for the letter *b*. Collect things whose names begin with the sound for *b*. Together you can write a story that includes all the things you found.

91

I have a

_____

b<u>ug</u> m<u>ug</u>.

The b<u>ug</u> d<u>ug</u>.

Nighttime

Golden Bear
PHONICS/DECODING Phonogram: *-ug*

Read the sentences with children and have them trace the letters to complete each word. Then have them read the completed sentences and draw pictures to illustrate them.

92

"I __have__ a  ."

"I __have__ a ."

I have a _____ .

Ira Sleeps Over

Golden Bear

Nighttime

Golden Bear
VOCABULARY High-Frequency Words: *have*

Read aloud the story titles under the boys' pictures. Have children trace the word *have* to complete the sentences. Ask them to paste the *Ira Sleeps Over* picture beside the sentence that Ira might say and to paste the *Golden Bear* picture beside the sentence that the boy in that story might say. Have children write or dictate words to tell what **they** have for the last sentence.

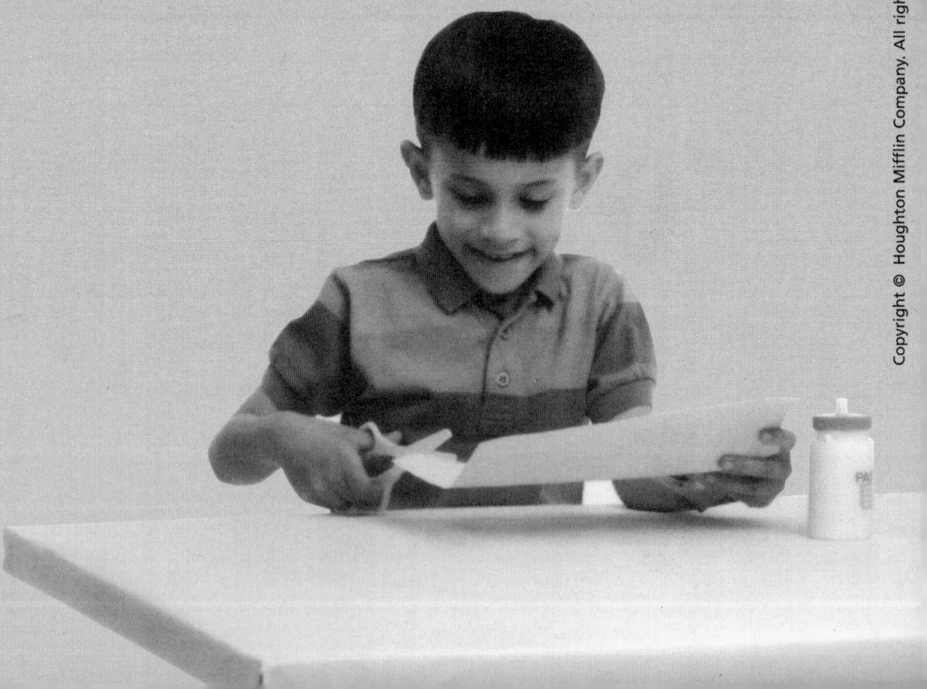

Nighttime

Where Does the Brown Bear Go?
PERSONAL RESPONSE

Children draw a nighttime picture of their favorite place mentioned or shown in the story. They may wish to write or dictate a sentence about their picture.

Where does _____ go?

Where does _____ go?

Where Does the Brown Bear Go?
LANGUAGE PATTERNS

Using the sentence pattern from the story, children think of a pet, toy animal, or person they would like to write about. They draw a picture of the one they have chosen. Then they write or dictate words to complete the sentence. They may wish to also write or dictate an answer to the question.

Nighttime

Nighttime

Where Does the Brown Bear Go?
COMPREHENSION Story Structure: Setting

Help children to name the animals (monkey, camel, sea gull, bear) and to identify the places that were in the story (desert, forest, sea, jungle). Then have them paste each animal in the kind of place where it was shown in the story.

g g g

Where Does the Brown Bear Go?
PHONICS/DECODING *g*

Have children think of the sound at the beginning of the Magic Picture *ghost* as they name and trace the letter *g* at the top of the page. Ask them to color pictures of things near the garage whose names begin with the sound for *g* (*guitar, gate, game, golf clubs, gum, goose*) and to print the letter *g* on the garage door.

Nighttime

"Go, 🐱," said a 👨. .

"Go, 🐱," said a 👨. .

"My 🐱!" said a 👧. .

Nighttime

Where Does the Brown Bear Go?
VOCABULARY High-Frequency Words: *go, a*

Read aloud with children the sentence in the first speech balloon. Ask children to trace the words *go* and *a* to complete the sentences in the speech balloons. Then have them read what the man and the girl said.

"Go hug a bug!" said my .

"Go hug a !" I said.

Dear Family,

Play a bedtime game with your child. Hide a stuffed toy and ask, "Where has (toy's name) gone tonight?" Have your child guess where it may have gone. Then give clues to help your child find it.

④

FOLD HERE

My Bear, My Bug

"I have bug ," said my .

"I have ," I said.

◇1

"I have a bug mug," said my .

"I have a  mug," I said.

"My 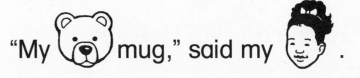 mug," said my .

"**MY** mug," I said.

2

3

Jamaica's Find
PERSONAL RESPONSE
Have children draw a picture of something they have found and kept. Encourage children to write or dictate a sentence about their picture.

Let's Be Friends

Dear Family,
Invite your child to tell you about the story *Jamaica's Find*. Talk about a toy or other possession that is special to your child. Then share with your child something that was special to you when you were his or her age.

103

Jamaica's Find

COMPREHENSION Inferences: Making Predictions

Talk with children about Jamaica's feelings when she found the stuffed dog and how her feelings changed. Invite children to use what they know about Jamaica to draw a picture showing what might happen the next time she finds something. You may wish to have children write or dictate a sentence about their drawing.

Let's Be Friends

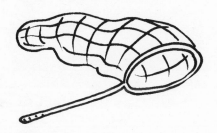

Let's Be Friends

Jamaica's Find
PHONEMIC AWARENESS Beginning Sounds

Children name the two pictures in each row (*duck, log; net, jar; hook, bike*). Then they listen as you say a word and color the picture whose name has the same beginning sound as the word you say. Say these words: (row 1) **dog**, (row 2) **jet**, (row 3) **book**.

What Shall We Do When We All Go Out?
PERSONAL RESPONSE

Children draw a picture to show what the brother and sister in the selection did that they too would like to do. They might wish to write or dictate a sentence about the drawing.

Let's Be Friends

106

_____

- -

We will _____

When we all go out to play!

What Shall We Do When We All Go Out?
LANGUAGE PATTERNS
Children draw something that they have fun doing with a friend. Then they write or dictate the name of the activity to complete the language pattern from the selection.

Let's Be Friends

107

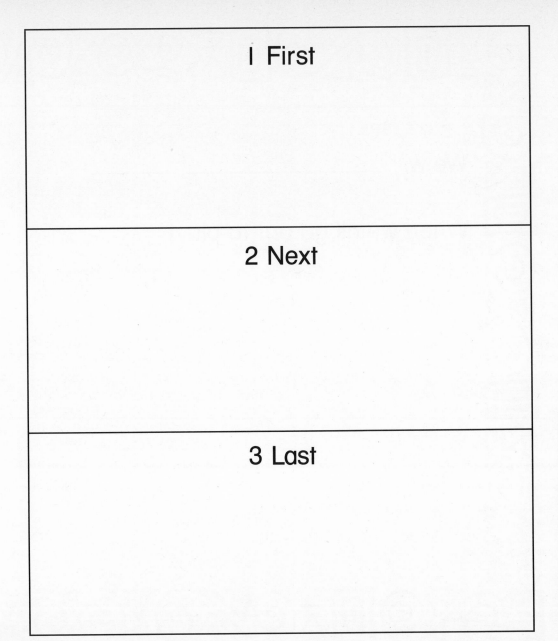

1 First
2 Next
3 Last

What Shall We Do When We All Go Out?
COMPREHENSION Sequence

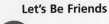

Read the numbers and order words with children. Have them name each meal shown (lunch, breakfast, dinner) and draw a line from it to the box with the number and order word that tells in what part of the day the meal comes. Ask them to draw one thing in box 1 that the brother and sister did after breakfast, one thing in box 2 that they did after lunch, and one thing in box 3 that they might do after dinner.

Let's Be Friends

What Shall We Do When We All Go Out?
PHONICS/DECODING *f*
Children think of the sound at the beginning of the Magic Picture *fish* as they name, trace, and print the letter *f* at the top of the page. Then they search for and color pictures on the leaves whose names begin with the sound for *f* (*feather, fan, five, feet, fox, fork, fence*).

Dear Family,
We have been learning about *f* and the sound it stands for. Play a guessing game by taking turns describing things whose names begin with the sound for *f*. Guess the words and write them on a list to read together.

109

I go ___in___ a 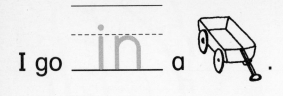.

I go ___in___ a .

I go ___in___ a 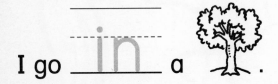.

Let's Be Friends

What Shall We Do When We All Go Out?
VOCABULARY High-Frequency Words: *in*

Suggest that children first read the sentences with a partner. Then have them trace the word *in* to complete each sentence. Invite children to choose which activity they would most like to do with a friend and draw a picture of it. You may wish to have them write or dictate a sentence to tell more about the activity.

110

Let's Be Friends

Together
PERSONAL RESPONSE

Children draw a picture to show themselves and a friend doing something they might think about doing together. They may wish to write or dictate a sentence describing what they drew.

You _____
- -
_____

and I'll _____.

Let's Be Friends

Together
LANGUAGE PATTERNS

Ask children to think about the story *Together* and then draw a picture of themselves and a friend doing something real or make-believe. Invite them to write or dictate what each is doing in the illustration to complete the sentence. Explain to children that their friends are "You" and they are the "I'll" in the sentence.

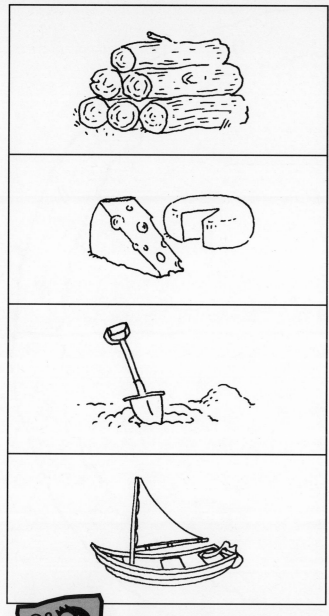

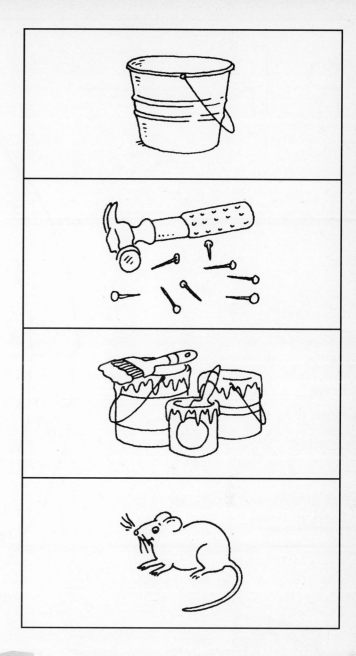

Let's Be Friends

Together
COMPREHENSION Noting Details

Children recall what the friends in the story dreamed of doing together and then they name and color the pictures (timber, cheese, shovel, boat; pail, hammer and nails, paint, mouse). Then they draw lines to match the details from the selection that go together.

p   p   p

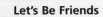

Together
PHONICS/DECODING *p*

Children think of the sound at the beginning of the Magic Picture *pig* as they name and trace the letter *p* at the top of the page. Then they draw pizza toppings whose names begin with the sound for *p* (the toppings need not be food) and write the letter *p* on the lines in each piece of pizza. They can draw additional toppings in the empty space beside the pizza.

Let's Be Friends

114

I <u>**dig**</u> in the 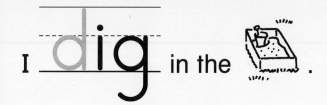 .

I put a <u>**pig**</u> in the .

I go in a <u>**big**</u> .

Let's Be Friends

Together
PHONICS/DECODING Phonogram: *-ig*
Children trace the initial consonant letters to complete the words. They read the
sentences and draw a picture to illustrate one of them. Children can add details to the
picture to show how a friend might help them.

"I __put__ in the 🍌 ," said the 👧 .

"I __put__ in the 🍓 ," said the 👦 .

"I __put__ in the 🥜 ," said the 👧 .

Together
VOCABULARY High-Frequency Words: *put*
Children trace the word *put* to complete each sentence. Then they read the story and draw a picture of what the boy and girl might have made with the banana, the strawberries, and the nuts.

Let's Be Friends

116

"Have a fig," said Ned.

"A big fig!" said Min.

Dear Family,
Talk together about things you and your child can accomplish when you work together. Make plans to do something together. Write out your plan and post it as a reminder of what you will do.

4

FOLD HERE

The Fig Tree

"I have the 🌱," said Ned.

"I have the 🔨," said Min.

1

"I put in the ," said Ned.

"I put in the ," said Min.

2

"I have a big ," said Ned.

"I put in the ," said Min.

3

FOLD HERE

Playful Pets

I Have a Pet!
PERSONAL RESPONSE

Children draw pictures they think would be in the window of the pet shop. They write the name of a pet they would like to have on the lines below the window.

Dear Family,

Cut pictures from old magazines, and work with your child to make a scrapbook of pets. See how many different kinds of pets you can find.

Children may wish to draw a picture of their own here.

Playful Pets

I Have a Pet!
COMPREHENSION Compare and Contrast

Ask children to identify the animals and to decide which animal in the cut-and-paste boxes is most like the dog. Have them paste that animal in the column with the dog. Then have children draw in the same column, an animal that is very different from the dog. Repeat for the bird.

121

Playful Pets

Hunky Dory Found It
PERSONAL RESPONSE

Children draw pictures to show what Hunky Dory might do if he followed his owner to school one day. Children may wish to write or dictate a sentence to tell about their picture.

_____

- -

_____ Lin

lost a

Hunky Dory found it.

_____

- -

_____ Pat

dropped a

Hunky Dory found it.

Hunky Dory Found It
LANGUAGE PATTERNS

Children extend the language pattern from the story by writing a first name to finish the sentence on the left. Then they think of something that might have been lost and draw a picture to illustrate their idea. They write another first name to finish the sentence on the right and draw something the person might have dropped.

Playful Pets

124

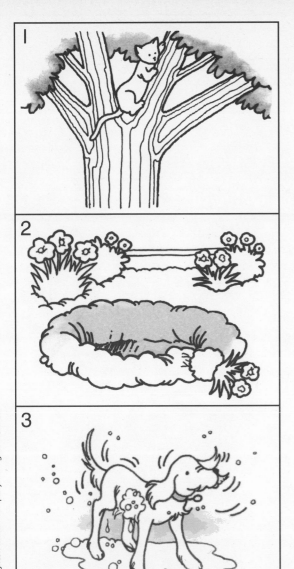

Playful Pets

Hunky Dory Found It
COMPREHENSION Cause and Effect

Children tell what has happened in picture 1. (A cat has climbed up a tree.) They find the picture in the last column that shows what caused that to happen and cut and paste it in the space beside picture 1. Repeat for pictures 2 and 3 to show what caused the hole to be in the garden and what caused the dog to be wet and soapy.

k

Playful Pets

Hunky Dory Found It
PHONICS/DECODING *k*

Children think of the sound at the beginning of the Magic Picture *king* as they name and trace the letter *k* at the top of the page. They name the items collected in the sack and color each one whose name begins with the sound for *k* (keys, kangaroo, kite). Then they write the letter *k* beside each picture they color.

Dear Family,
We have been learning about the letter *k* and the sound it stands for. In storybooks that you read together, look for words that begin with the letter *k* and have the same beginning sound as the word *king*.

127

hit fit sit

_____

- - - - - - - - - - - - - - - - - - -

"A _____!" said Tommy.

_____

- - - - - - - - - - - - - - - - - - -

"I said _____ ," said Julie.

_____

- - - - - - - - - - - - - - - - - - -

"I _____ ," said Amy.

Playful Pets

Hunky Dory Found It
PHONICS/DECODING Phonogram: *-it*
Children trace the letters at the top of the page to make words with the phonogram
-it. Then, choosing from these words, they complete each sentence so that it tells
about the picture beside it.

it

"I have _____ ," said Hunky Dory.

Ann hit _____.

I put _____ in.

Playful Pets

Hunky Dory Found It
VOCABULARY **High-Frequency Words:** *it*
Children trace the word *it* at the top of the page. Then they write *it* to complete the sentences. Finally they circle in each picture what "it" is.

Playful Pets

Snow on Snow on Snow
PERSONAL RESPONSE

Children draw a picture to show the part of the story they liked best. They may wish to write the title of the story below their picture.

Once upon a winter's day

I

Once upon a summer's day

I

Playful Pets

Snow on Snow on Snow
LANGUAGE PATTERNS

Children tell what time of year is shown in each picture and think about what they once did on a winter's day and on a summer's day. Children may wish to write or dictate what they did to complete the language pattern from the story and then illustrate their sentences.

131

Playful Pets

132

Snow on Snow on Snow
COMPREHENSION Sequence

Explain that each pair of pictures tells a story. Ask children to tell what is happening in each pair of pictures and to color in the one that shows what probably happens first. Have children make up and tell stories to classmates using the picture pairs as prompts.

C  C

Snow on Snow on Snow
PHONICS/DECODING c

Children think of the sound at the beginning of the Magic Picture *cat* as they name and trace the letter c at the top of the page. Then they write the letter c by those pictures whose names begin with the same sound as cat (*cage, cattails, camera, carrot, cup, cane*). Finally they lightly color the puzzle pieces in which they have written c to form a cat.

Playful Pets

did

The cat _____ it!

My pet _____ it!

I _____ it!

Snow on Snow on Snow
VOCABULARY High-Frequency Words: *did*
Children trace the word *did*. They write *did* to complete each sentence and then read the sentences to describe the pictures.

Playful Pets

134

"I did it!" said Paco.

Dear Family,
Take turns with your child drawing animals that might make good pets.

Sit, Kit!

"Kit bit my ," said Paco.

"Sit, Kit!" said Father.

Kit did.

"Kit hit my ," said Tina.

"Sit, Kit!" said Father.

Kit did.

"The ⬤⬤!" said Father.

"Kit!" said Mother.

FOLD HERE

I can _____ !

Whistle for Willie
PERSONAL RESPONSE

Children draw a picture showing themselves learning to do something new. After hearing the sentence starter, *I can ___!* read aloud, they write or dictate words to complete the sentence so it tells about their picture.

I Can Do Anything

Dear Family,
Invite your child to tell you about the story *Whistle for Willie*. Talk about some things he or she would like to learn to do. Then share with your child what seemed important for you to learn when you were your child's age.

137

I Can Do Anything

Whistle for Willie
COMPREHENSION Story Structure

Children color the picture that shows a child trying to do what Peter tries to do in the story *Whistle for Willie*. Have them draw a picture of what happens next to the child.

Whistle for Willie
PHONEMIC AWARENESS First Sounds of Spoken Words

For the first three windows, help children name what is pictured there (*camera, cat, flowers; guitar, tiger, game; book, dog, doll*). Have them color in each of these windows the two things that begin with the same sound. For the last window, have them name the item (*ball*) and draw a picture of something else that begins with the same sound.

I Can Do Anything

139

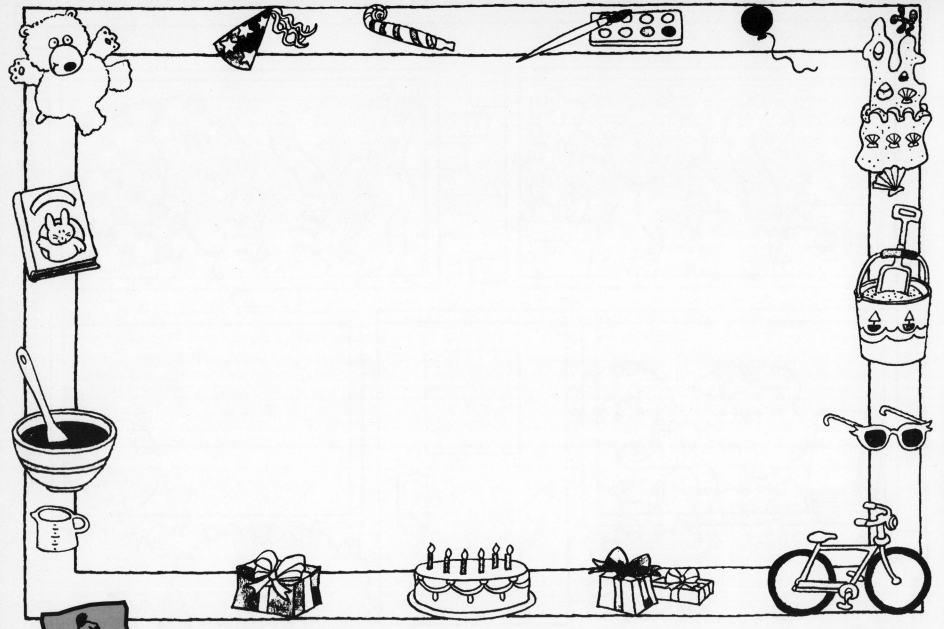

Things I Like
PERSONAL RESPONSE

Children use clues in the border of the page to help them recall some of the things the monkey in the story liked. Then they choose something they like to do or would like to try, and draw a picture of themselves doing that. Children may wish to write or dictate a sentence about their picture.

I Can Do
Anything

140

This is me,

and this is what **I** like:

_____

- -

_____

I Can Do Anything

Things I Like
LANGUAGE PATTERNS

As you read the language pattern from the story, children think of a page they would write and illustrate for a book titled *Things I Like.* They draw a picture of themselves and the activity and write or dictate the name of the activity to complete the language pattern from the story.

Things I Like

COMPREHENSION Story Structure: Character

Tell children that it is the little monkey's birthday and that they should use what they know about the monkey from the story to help them choose a special present for him. Have them draw a picture of the present they chose. Then ask them to write a name for the monkey on the tag.

I Can Do Anything

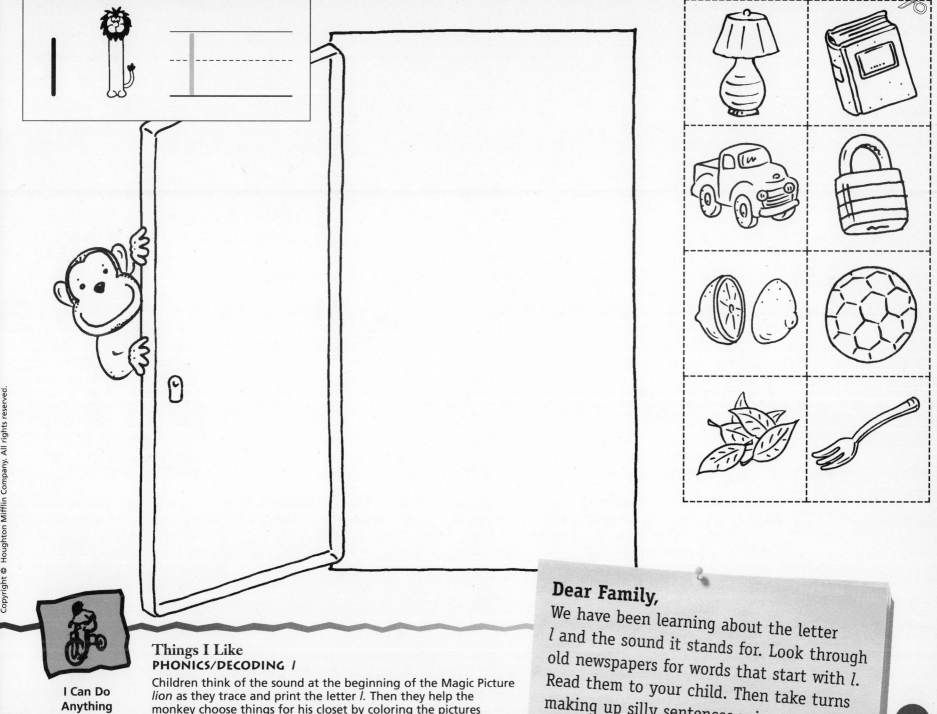

Things I Like
PHONICS/DECODING /

Children think of the sound at the beginning of the Magic Picture
lion as they trace and print the letter *l*. Then they help the
monkey choose things for his closet by coloring the pictures
whose names begin with the sound for *l* (*lamp, lock, lemon, leaves*) and pasting those pictures in the closet.

I Can Do Anything

Dear Family,
We have been learning about the letter
l and the sound it stands for. Look through
old newspapers for words that start with *l*.
Read them to your child. Then take turns
making up silly sentences using as many of
the words as you can.

143

I put my h<u>and</u> in it.

I l<u>and</u> in the s<u>and</u>.

I like the b<u>and</u>.

I Can Do Anything

Things I Like

PHONICS/DECODING Phonogram: *-and*

Children trace the phonogram *-and* to complete the word in each sentence. Then they read each sentence and draw a line from the sentence to the picture that goes with it.

I like   .

I like  and  .

I like  and _____ and _____ .

I Can Do Anything

Things I Like
VOCABULARY High-Frequency Words: *like, and*

Children trace the words *like* and *and* to complete the sentences. They draw pictures of a kind of animal they like and write or dictate a word to complete the last sentence.

Quick as a Cricket
PERSONAL RESPONSE

Children draw a picture of themselves doing something with an animal from the story. They may wish to write or dictate a sentence describing their illustration.

I Can Do Anything

I'm as large as

_____

- -

_____.

I Can Do Anything

148

Quick as a Cricket
LANGUAGE PATTERNS

Ask children to compare themselves to an animal that is much larger than they are and to draw a picture of themselves standing next to that animal. Then have them write or dictate the words that complete the language pattern from the story.

I Can Do Anything

Quick as a Cricket
COMPREHENSION Story Structure: Setting

Have children identify the animals mentioned in the story (whale, basset, chimp, cricket). Help them identify the four settings where these animals might be found (in the sea, in a home, in a yard, in a jungle). Ask children to cut and paste each animal in the place where it was in the story.

t

I Can Do Anything

Quick as a Cricket
PHONICS/DECODING *t*

Have children think of the sound at the beginning of the Magic Picture *tiger* as they name and trace the letter *t*. Tell them they can play tick-tack-toe by coloring each picture whose name begins with the sound for *t* (*turtle, tiger, tire, tent, table*) and writing the letter *t* on the lines below it. Explain that when they are through, they will have colored three pictures across and three down.

Children may wish to draw a picture of their own here.

"My  and I like

the band," said  .

Dear Family,
Talk together about something new your child can do that he or she is proud of. Together, make a chart on which the two of you can record and review his or her daily accomplishments.

4

FOLD HERE

The Band

"My  and I have

a band," said .

1

"I like the  in the band,"

said  .

"And I like the in the band,"

said .

"I like the in the band,"

said .

"And I like the in the band,"

said  .

2

3

Here Come the Bears

Two Bear Cubs
PERSONAL RESPONSE
Have children draw a picture to show something they learned about bears while reading *Two Bear Cubs*. Encourage them to write or dictate a sentence about their pictures.

Dear Family,
Invite your child to tell you what he or she learned about bears in the story *Two Bear Cubs*. You may want to visit your public library together to find and read other books about real bears.

Here Come the Bears

Two Bear Cubs
COMPREHENSION Supporting Details

Have children recall some of the things the bear cubs did. Then ask them to draw a picture of one of the activities they named.

Here Come the Bears

Two Bear Cubs
PHONEMIC AWARENESS Last Sounds of Words

Children name the pictures in each row, listening for the last sounds in each word (*bear, book, chair; bees, trees, balls; fork, fish, dish; skate, skunk, gate*). They color the two pictures in the row whose names have the same last sounds.

157

Just Like Daddy
PERSONAL RESPONSE

Children draw a picture to show what they would like to do—just like someone else.
Encourage children to write or dictate a sentence about their drawing.

Here Come the Bears

158

I put a big worm on my hook...
Just like Daddy.

_____

- -

I _____...

_____

- -

Just like _____.

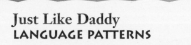

**Here Come
the Bears**

Just Like Daddy
LANGUAGE PATTERNS

Help children read the sentence pattern from the story. Have them draw something
else the bear cub did just like his daddy. Then have children write or dictate words to
complete the sentence pattern that their picture illustrates.

Just Like Daddy
COMPREHENSION Story Structure: Beginning, Middle, End

Ask children to recall events from the story *Just Like Daddy*. Have them describe the picture in the middle of the page. Explain that this shows something that happened in the middle of the story. Then ask them to draw a picture in the first space that shows what happened at the beginning of the story and a picture in the last space that shows the end.

Here Come the Bears

160

W

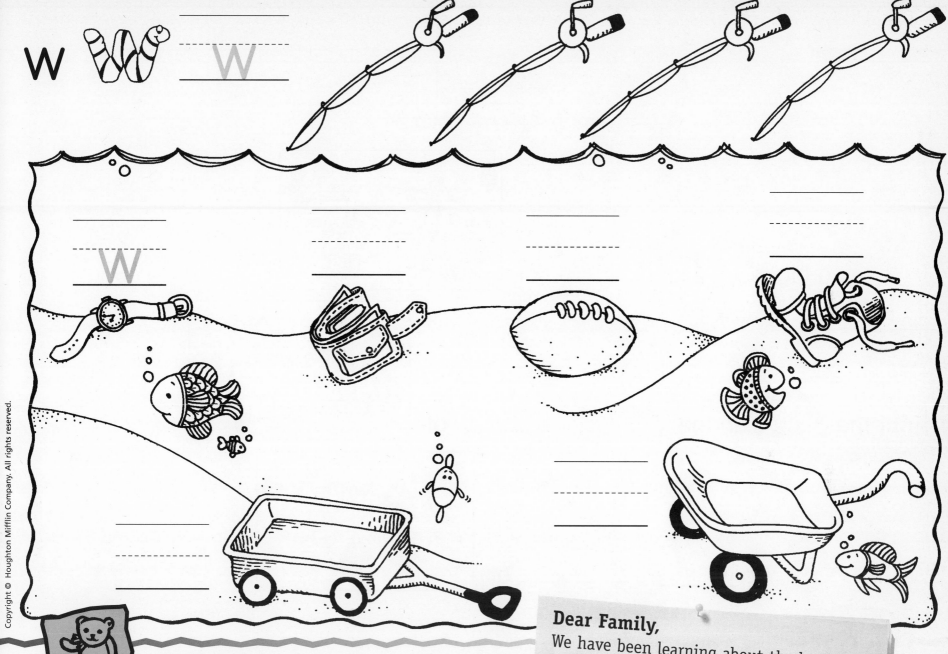

Here Come the Bears

Just Like Daddy
PHONICS/DECODING *w*
Children think of the beginning sound of the Magic Picture *worm* as they name and trace the letter *w*. They name the items (*watch, wallet, football, boot, wagon, wheelbarrow*), color the ones whose names begin with the sound for *w* and write *w* beside them.

Dear Family,
We have been learning about the letter *w* and one of the sounds it stands for. Take turns thinking of words that start with the sound for *w*. Together illustrate each word and write the word below the picture.

161

g   l   p

I _____ a big . _____ ot

I put the in the _____. _____ ot

We like a _____. _____ ot

Here Come the Bears

Just Like Daddy
PHONICS/DECODING Phonogram : *-ot*
Children trace each letter in the box at the top of the page. To complete each
sentence, they write one of the letters beside the phonogram *-ot* to make a word that
makes sense in the sentence.

 like  .

 like  .

like _____ .

_____

_____ like

_____ .

W̲e̲ like  .

W̲e̲ like  .

Here Come the Bears

Just Like Daddy
VOCABULARY **High-Frequency Words:** *we*

For each of the first two columns, children tell about the picture, read the first sentence, and trace the word *we* to complete the second sentence. For the third column, children think of something else that bears and children might both like and illustrate their idea. Then they write or dictate the words to complete the sentence.

163

This Is the Bear and the Picnic Lunch
PERSONAL RESPONSE

Children draw a picture of a time when something they planned didn't work out the way they thought it would. They should include themselves in the picture and show how they felt. They may wish to write or dictate a sentence about how they felt.

Here Come the Bears

164

This is the _____

who _____.

**Here Come
the Bears**

This Is the Bear and the Picnic Lunch
LANGUAGE PATTERNS

Read the language pattern from the story with children, substituting the word *blank* where there are writing lines. Have children think of an animal name and an action word to complete the sentence. Ask them to draw a picture to illustrate their idea. Then have them write or dictate words to complete the sentence so that it tells about their picture.

Here Come the Bears

This Is the Bear and the Picnic Lunch
COMPREHENSION Fantasy and Realism

Children tell what is happening in the pictures. They cut and paste in the first column the pictures that show things that might happen in real life. They cut and paste in the second column the pictures that show things that could only happen in a make-believe story.

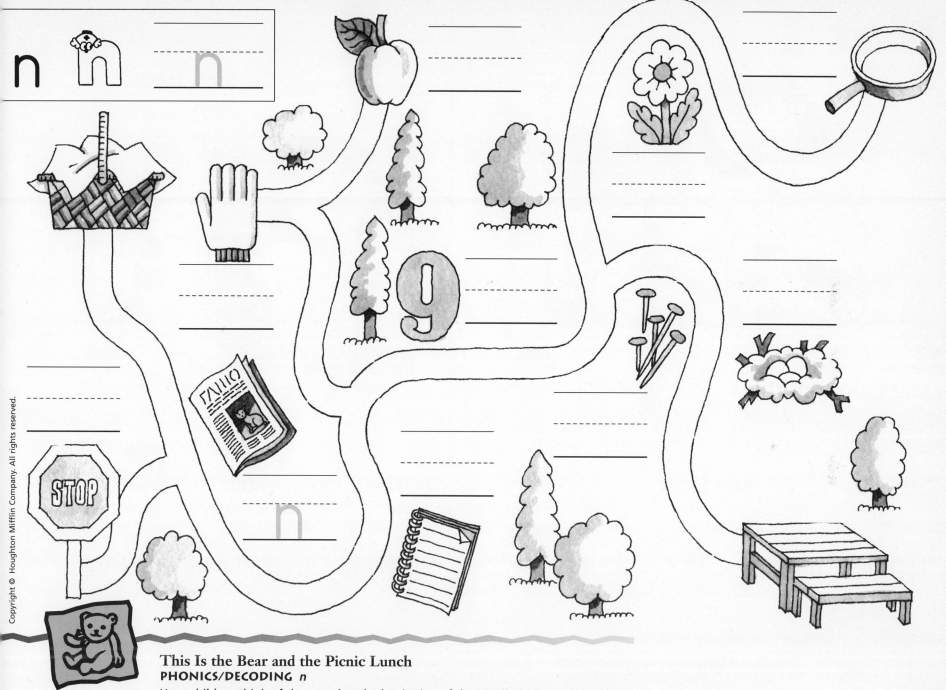

This Is the Bear and the Picnic Lunch
PHONICS/DECODING *n*

Have children think of the sound at the beginning of the Magic Picture *nurse* as they name and trace the letter at the top of the page. Ask them to color each picture whose name begins with the sound for *n* and to write the letter *n* on the lines by each (*newspaper, notebook, nine, nails, nest*). Then have them draw a line through the maze from the basket to the table.

Here Come the Bears

169

Not I

"Did Dog get my ?" said the .

" <u>Not</u> I," said Dog.

"Did Bear get my ?" said the .

" <u>Not</u> I," said Bear.

"Dog! Bear!" said the .

"**We** got it," said Dog and Bear.

This Is the Bear and the Picnic Lunch
VOCABULARY High-Frequency Words: *not*
Children trace the word *not* to complete the sentences. Then they read the story.

**Here Come
the Bears**

170

We got in the  .

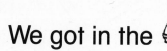 did not!

Dear Family,
Talk with your child about all the stories he or she knows that involve bears. Take turns telling each other one of the stories and decide if the stories are about real or make-believe bears.

4

FOLD HERE

The Bear Got It

 got the  .

We did not.

1

 got the .

We did not.

FOLD HERE

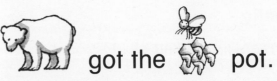 got the pot.

We did not.

2

3

Going Places

The Wheels on the Bus
PERSONAL RESPONSE
Invite children to draw a picture of their favorite part of the song. Then have them write or dictate something below their picture to tell about it.

Dear Family,
Talk with your child about riding a bus, a subway, or other forms of transportation. Then, using chairs, take turns as driver and passengers. Sing "The Wheels on the Bus" as you play, making up new words to fit your type of transportation.

The Wheels on the Bus
COMPREHENSION Cause and Effect

Discuss each picture with children. Then have them color the dog. Next ask them to decide which picture in the bottom row shows what happened because the dog was sitting in the street and to draw a line to connect the two pictures. Have children complete the page the same way for the pictures of the rain and the nails.

Going Places

174

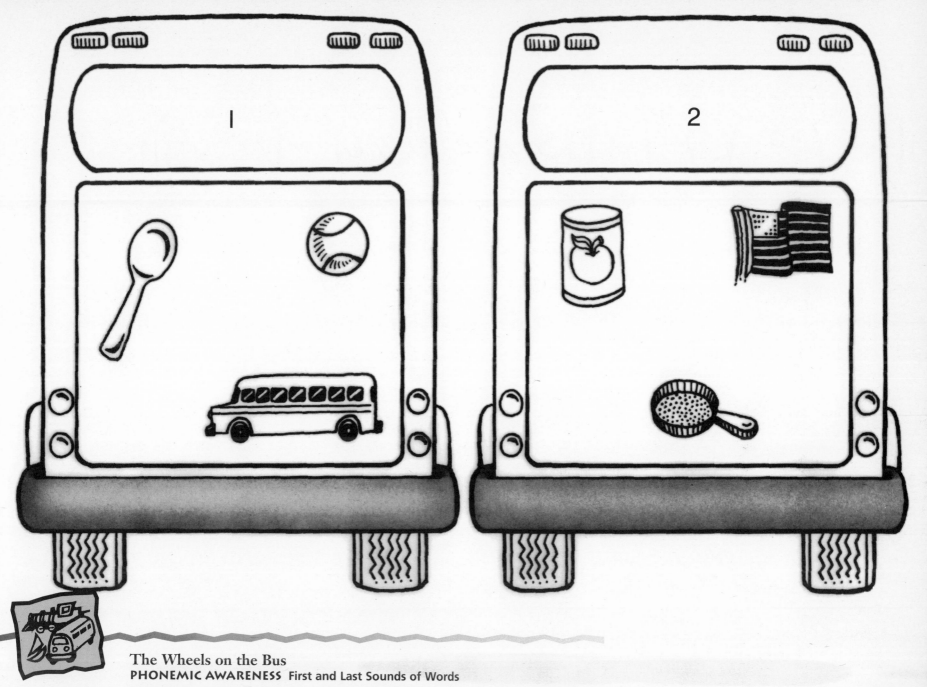

The Wheels on the Bus

PHONEMIC AWARENESS First and Last Sounds of Words

Going Places

Have children name each picture on the back of bus number 1 *(spoon, baseball, bus)*. Ask them to circle the two pictures whose names begin with the same sound. Repeat for the pictures on bus number 2 *(can, pan, flag)*, having children draw lines under the two pictures whose names have the same last sounds.

Children may wish to draw a picture of their own here.

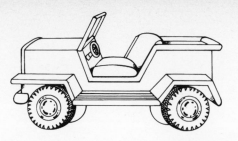

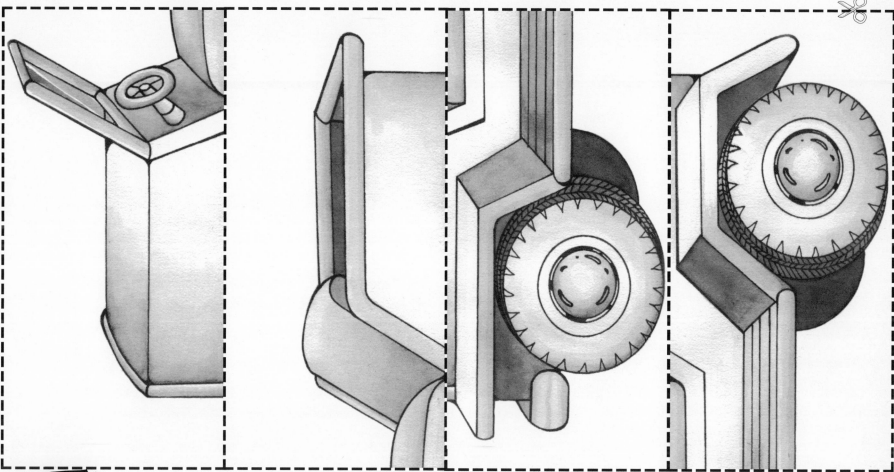

Going Places

Sheep in a Jeep
PERSONAL RESPONSE

Children paste the page onto a piece of heavy paper. They then cut on the broken lines and put the puzzle pieces together to form a jeep like the one shown at the top of the page. Children use their assembled puzzle to illustrate as they retell the story *Sheep in a Jeep* in their own words.

178

Sheep in a _____

_____

Jet

Van

Train

Boat

Going Places

Sheep in a Jeep
LANGUAGE PATTERNS
Children choose something else the sheep might take a ride in and write the name of that vehicle to finish the title. They think of something silly that the sheep might do in the vehicle and illustrate their idea.

Sheep in a Jeep
COMPREHENSION Sequence

Tell children they will draw a line along the road from the START to the FINISH. Say, **Help the sheep get to the finish by going only on roads that show things that happen in the story. Be careful not to go on the other roads.**

Going Places

JUNK

Sheep in a Jeep
PHONICS/DECODING *j*

Going Places

Have children think of the sound at the beginning of the Magic Picture *jack-in-the-box* as they name and trace the letter *j*. Ask them to color each thing in the junkyard whose name begins with the sound for *j* (*jeep, jacket, jump rope, jacks, jar*) and to write the letter *j* on the lines beside the pictures they color.

Dear Family,

We have been learning about the letter *j* and the sound it stands for. On a trip to the market with your child, see how many things you can find that begin with *j*. When you get home, write a list of the things you found.

181

__G__et __W__et

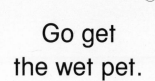

Go get
the wet pet.

Sheep get wet!

Sheep get set.

Sheep in a Jeep
PHONICS/DECODING Phonogram: *-et*
Children identify the phonogram *-et* and trace the letters beside *-et* to complete the words in the title. They read aloud the title. Then they read the sentences and paste each one under the picture it tells about.

Going Places

183

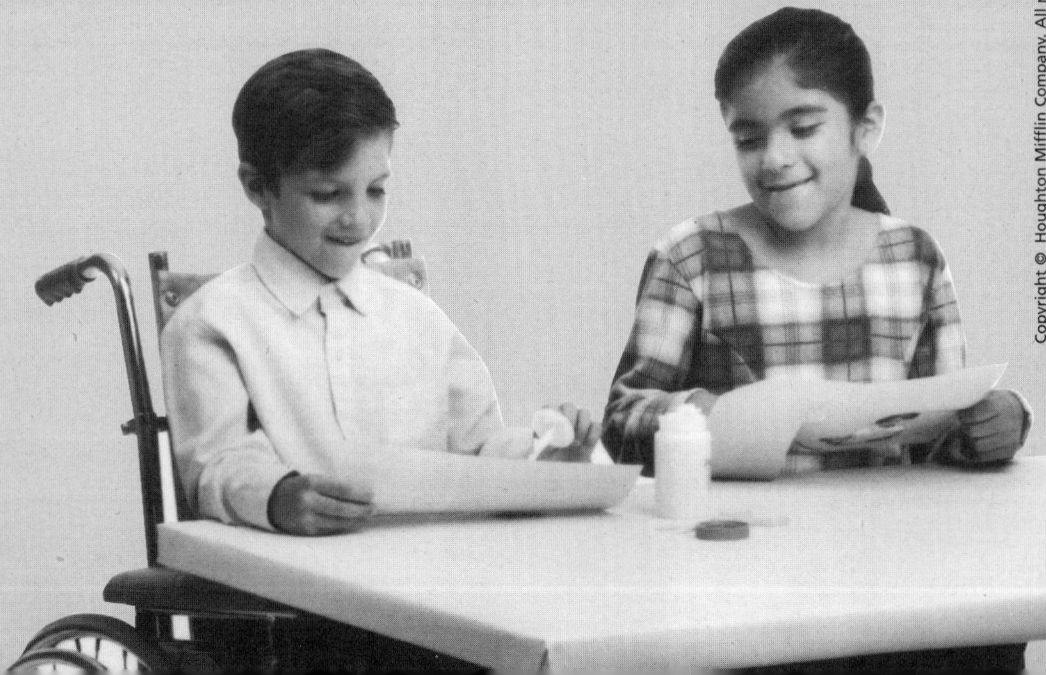

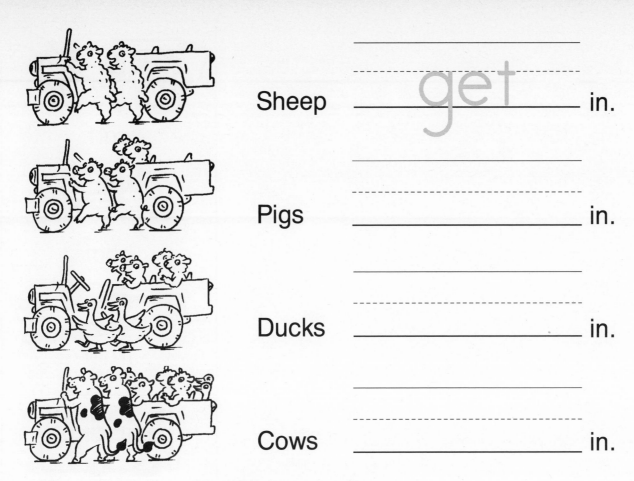

Sheep _____ get _____ in.

Pigs _____ in.

Ducks _____ in.

Cows _____ in.

Going Places

Sheep in a Jeep
VOCABULARY High-Frequency Words: *get*

Discuss the first picture and read the sentence aloud with children. Have them trace the high-frequency word *get*. Ask children to complete each of the remaining sentences by writing the word *get*. Then have them read the sentences.

185

I can ___ go .

cart

boat

train

bus

rocket

I can go in a _____ .

On the Go
PERSONAL RESPONSE

Going Places

Read the first sentence aloud with children, having them trace the word *go*. Then have them choose a means of transportation from those shown and draw a picture of themselves riding in it. Ask them to complete the sentence at the bottom of the page with the word that names the vehicle they drew.

You can go on a  .

You can go on a

You can go on a

Going Places

On the Go
LANGUAGE PATTERNS
Ask children to recall the different ways people in the selection move about. Read the first sentence aloud, pausing to allow children to say the word the rebus stands for. Have them draw their own rebus pictures to complete the remaining sentences. Then encourage them to write or dictate one more sentence with the same pattern.

187

How People Go Places   We Go to School

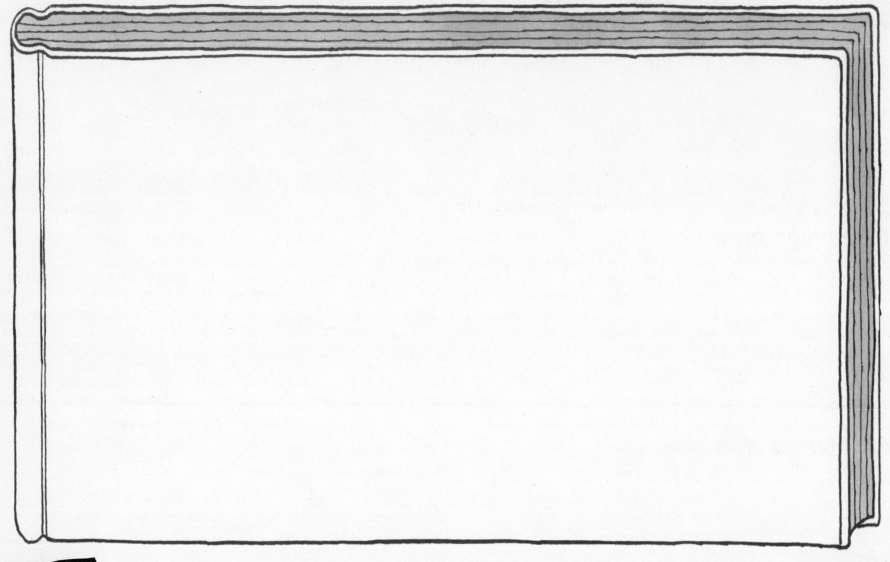

Going Places

On the Go
COMPREHENSION Main Idea
Read aloud the two titles and have children underline the one that tells what *On the Go* is all about. Then have each child draw something that could be used as a picture on a book titled *How People Go Places*. Children may wish to write or dictate something about their cover picture.

188

On the Go
PHONICS/DECODING *r*

Have children think of the sound at the beginning of the Magic Picture *rocket* as they name and trace the letter *r* at the top of the page. Have them start at the raft and draw the route the raft will follow to the dock. Ask them to color each picture along the river whose name begins with the sound for *r* (*raft, rake, robot, ring, rabbit*) and to write *r* on the lines beside the pictures they color.

Going Places

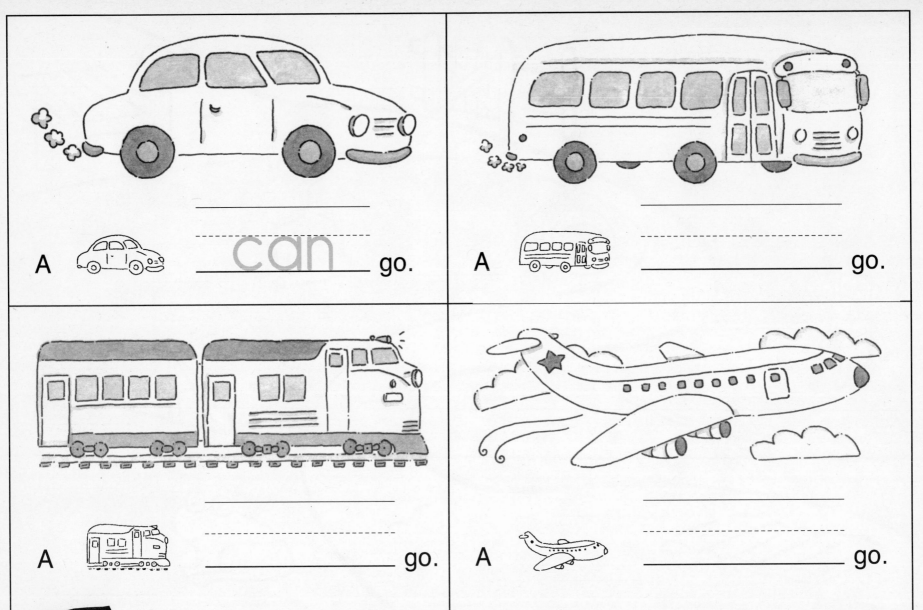

A  _can_ go.

A _____ go.

A _____ go.

A _____ go.

On the Go
VOCABULARY High-Frequency Words: *can*
Children trace the word *can* and read the first sentence. Then they write *can* to complete the remaining sentences that are captions for the pictures.

Going Places

Dad said, "Ellen, go get in a ."

Dear Family,
The next time you and your child go somewhere together, notice how many different kinds of vehicles you see. When you get home, draw pictures of what you saw.

4

FOLD HERE

HATS TO GO

Ellen said, "I can get in a ."

1

Ellen said, "I can go get a ."

2

Ellen said, "I can get in a jet."

3

FOLD HERE

The Gingerbread Boy
PERSONAL RESPONSE

Invite children to draw a picture of their favorite scene from *The Gingerbread Boy*. Then have them write or dictate something to tell about their drawing.

Tell Me a Story

Dear Family,
Look in your local public library for different versions of *The Gingerbread Boy* (sometimes called *The Gingerbread Man*). Compare the art and the events in the versions you find.

193

The Gingerbread Boy
COMPREHENSION Inferences: Drawing Conclusions

Encourage children to select one of the characters from the story and have them draw a picture of the character in the box. Then in the thought balloon, have them draw a picture and write or dictate to show what the character is probably thinking about as he or she runs after the Gingerbread Boy.

Tell Me a Story

194

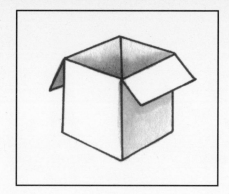

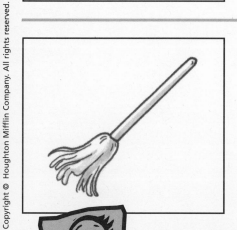

The Gingerbread Boy

PHONEMIC AWARENESS Blending Sounds

Tell Me a Story

Have children name the two pictures in the first row (fan, box). Say, **Think of the sound you hear at the beginning of** *fan* **and say it. Then think of the last sounds you hear in** *box* **and say them. Now put all of these sounds together to make a word. Say the word and then draw a picture of it** (fox). Repeat for girl and plate (gate) and for mop and fan (man).

Children may wish to draw a picture of their own here.

Three Little Kittens
PERSONAL RESPONSE
Children draw pictures to show what they think the kittens might do after they smell a rat. Children can compare their pictures with those of classmates.

Tell Me a Story

197

The three little kittens
lost their

The three little kittens
found their

Tell Me a Story

Three Little Kittens
LANGUAGE PATTERNS

Have children draw a picture of something else the kittens might have lost and then found again. You may wish to have them write or dictate a word to label their pictures and finish the sentence.

Three Little Kittens

COMPREHENSION Compare and Contrast

Have children tell what is happening in each picture and decide in which picture the kittens are behaving well enough for the mother cat to give them some pie. Have them cut and paste the happy mother cat and a pie below the picture that shows good behavior and a sad mother cat and the empty pie tin below the picture that shows bad behavior.

Tell Me a Story

y y y

Tell Me a Story

Three Little Kittens
PHONICS/DECODING y

Children think of the sound at the beginning of the Magic Picture *yarn* as they name and trace the letter *y* at the top of the page. Then they name the toys (*yo-yo, doll, yarn, ball, yak, bear*) and color in *yellow* each thing that begins with the sound for *y*. Finally they write the letter *y* by each picture they color.

Dear Family,
We have been learning about the letter *y* and the sound it stands for. On a shopping trip with your child, try to find some items whose names begin with *y*. When you get home, write a list of the things you found.

201

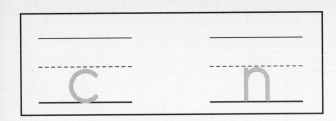

c   n

_____ut   "I can _____," said the cat.

_____ut   "I have a _____," said the cat.

Tell me a Story

Three Little Kittens
PHONICS/DECODING Phonogram: *-ut*

Have children trace the letters at the top of the page. Next, have them write one of these letters beside the phonogram *-ut* to make a word that tells about the picture. Finally, have children complete each sentence with the word they completed.

202

Three Little Kittens
VOCABULARY High-Frequency Words: *you, but*

Tell Me a Story

Have children trace the words at the top of the page. Ask them to decide what is happening in the pictures and to think about whether the mother cat is happy with the kittens. Read the kittens' question with children. Then have them complete the mother cat's answer by writing *But* and *you* where they make sense.

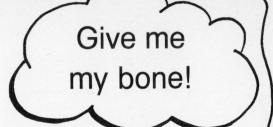

Give me
my bone!

Tell Me a Story

Teeny Tiny
PERSONAL RESPONSE

Children draw pictures to show what they would do if they were the teeny tiny woman in the story. Would they give up the bone, or would they think of some other way to get rid of the ghost?

204

Once upon a time,

there was a who

Once upon a time,

there was a who

Tell Me a Story

Teeny Tiny
LANGUAGE PATTERNS
Read aloud the beginning of the sentence pattern from the story, pausing at the picture for children to name the character. Have children complete the sentence by drawing something the teeny tiny woman does. To complete the second example, have children draw something else teeny tiny and what it might do. Children may wish to write or dictate something about their version of the sentence pattern.

Tell Me a Story

Teeny Tiny
COMPREHENSION Story Structure: Character, Setting, Ending
Help children identify the pictures in each box on the page (teeny tiny woman, giant, rabbit; bedroom, classroom, cave). Ask them to circle in the first box who the story was about and to circle in the second box where part of the story took place. Then ask them to draw a picture of what happened at the end of the story. Children may wish to write or dictate a sentence about the end of the story.

V v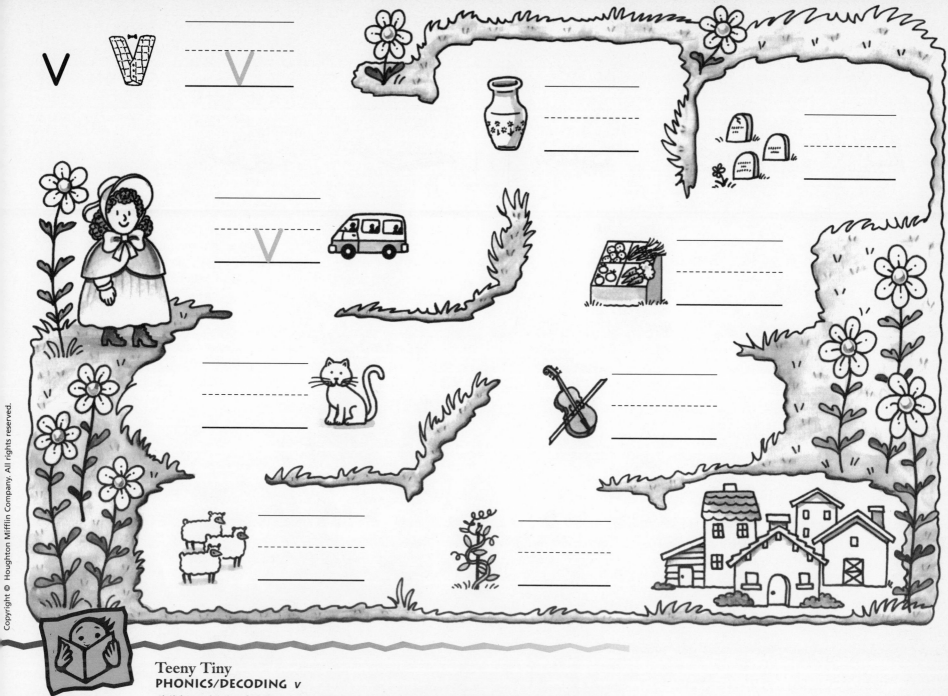

Teeny Tiny

PHONICS/DECODING *v*

Tell Me a Story

Children think of the sound at the beginning of the Magic Picture *vest* as they name and trace the letter *v* at the top of the page. They name the pictures and circle those whose names begin with the sound for *v* (*van, vase, vegetables, violin, vine*). They write the letter beside each picture they circled and draw a line to show the teeny tiny woman the way back to her village.

"Can I have it?" said Cat.

"Can I have it?" said Dog.

"Can I have it?" said Duck.

"Not you," said Red Hen,

"but I can!"

Dear Family,
Tell your child a familiar story you remember as a favorite when you were his or her age. Then take turns with your child changing something in the story to make a new version of it.

4

FOLD HERE

Can You Get It?

"Can you get a nut?" said Red Hen.

"Not I!" said Cat.

"Not I!" said Dog.

"Not I!" said Duck, "but you can."

1

"Can you cut the nut?"
said Red Hen.

"Not I!" said Cat.

"Not I!" said Dog.

"Not I!" said Duck, "but you can."

2

"Can you put it in the ?"
said Red Hen.

"Not I!" said Cat.

"Not I!" said Dog.

"Not I!" said Duck, "but you can."

3